THE LOVE ONE ANOTHER BIBLE STUDY SERIES

CONTRIBUTING
HELPING OTHERS FULFILL
THEIR POTENTIAL

A Bible Study by

Churches Alive!

MINISTERING TO THE CHURCHES OF THE WORLD
600 Meridian Avenue, Suite 200
San Jose, California 95126-3427

Published by

BRINGING TRUTH TO LIFE
NavPress Publishing Group
P.O. Box 35001, Colorado Springs, Colorado 80935

*Because we share kindred aims for helping local churches fulfill Christ's Great
Commission to "go and make disciples," NavPress and Churches Alive have
joined efforts on certain strategic publishing projects that are intended to bring
effective disciplemaking resources into the service of the local church.*

*For more than a decade, Churches Alive has teamed up with churches of all
denominations to establish vigorous disciplemaking ministries. At the same time,
NavPress has focused on publishing Bible studies, books, and other resources
that have grown out of The Navigators' 50 years of disciplemaking experience.*

*Now, together, we're working to offer special products like this one that are
designed to stimulate a deeper, more fruitful commitment to Christ in the local
gatherings of His Church.*

*The LOVE ONE ANOTHER series was written by Russ Korth, Ron Wormser, Jr., and
Ron Wormser, Sr. of Churches Alive. Many individuals from both Churches
Alive and NavPress contributed greatly in bringing this project to publication.*

Contents

Spiritual gifts do not come wrapped in colorful paper
and bright bows. They come wrapped in flesh.
God has gifted His children for special purposes.

Having Spiritual Gifts

▼

1 a. As a child, what was the most meaningful Christmas
present you received?

b. Was the value you placed on this gift proportionate to
the money spent on it? If not, what made it so valuable
to you?

2 Which Christians have spiritual gifts? (1 Corinthians 12:7)

3 How do you "get" a spiritual gift? (1 Corinthians 12:11; KJV—"severally" = "individually")

4 List the gifts from each passage below.

Romans 12:6-8

1 Corinthians 12:8-10 (KJV—"divers" = "various")

1 Corinthians 12:28

Ephesians 4:11

5 What significance do you attach to the fact that these lists of gifts are all slightly different?

6 What conclusion do you draw from the fact that the Bible contains no definite statement about how to know your spiritual gift(s)?

7 Although there is no clear teaching in Scripture on how to determine what gift(s) you have, you may find that answering the following questions will be helpful.

In doing things that contribute to others . . .

a. What do you enjoy doing?

b. What do you do well?

c. What do you do which brings pleasure to others?

d. In what areas do others say you are talented?

8 a. What do you think may be your gift(s)?

b. Name at least two people who have confirmed your conclusion.

9 a. How would you feel if you visited a friend in June and saw the birthday present you sent him or her last November unopened?

b. In what sense do some people leave the gifts God has
   given them unopened?

Christians are like plants. They grow when treated properly.
You can use your spiritual gifts to help others grow.

Using Spiritual Gifts

▼

1 a. What is one dream you have for your church fellowship?

b. What is one way using your gift can contribute to the fulfillment of this dream?

2 Why has God gifted you? (1 Corinthians 12:7)

3 How should you view yourself and your gift(s)? (Romans 12:3)

4 How should you use your gift(s)? (1 Peter 4:10-11)

5 What truths about spiritual gifts are illustrated by the human body in the following verses?

1 Corinthians 12:14-16

1 Corinthians 12:21-22

1 Corinthians 12:23-24

1 Corinthians 12:25-26

6 What benefits to the church result from the proper use of God's gifts? (Ephesians 4:11-16)

7 Compare the fruit of the Spirit listed in Galatians 5:22-23 with your lists of gifts of the Spirit in question 4 of lesson 1. What difference do you see between the fruit of the Spirit and gifts of the Spirit?

8 Complete the following sentences:

I am important to the growth and well-being of our church because . . .

I cannot be boastful or proud of the contribution I am making because . . .

9 a. How do you presently use God's gifts to you to contribute to the well-being of your church?

b. What additional ways can you use your gift(s)?

LESSON THREE
Contributing
with Good Works

▼

1 a. List at least three minor good deeds people did this past week for you.

b. What effect did these "little things" have on you?

2 Why is it important to do the "little things" for people? (Matthew 25:31-46)

15

3 a. For what are good deeds useful? (Titus 3:8)

b. For what are they not useful? (Titus 3:5)

4 How are good deeds related to salvation? (Ephesians 2:8-10)

5 Read Galatians 6:7-10.

a. What promises are associated with doing good deeds?

b. In your good deeds, who should have priority?

c. Why do you think God established this priority?

6 Read Matthew 5:14-16.

   a. What do you think it means to be set on a hill?

   b. In your opinion, who sets you on a hill?

   c. List some characteristics of light and explain how they illustrate living a Christian life in the world.

7 a. What are some things that help us shine as lights? (Philippians 2:14-16)

b. Can you think of a situation in the past month in which you grumbled? If so, briefly describe it.

8 What specific good deeds are mentioned in these verses?

Romans 12:13

1 Timothy 6:17-19

James 1:27

9 Study the situations and references listed here. After each situation, explain some creative ways you could demonstrate good works.

a. You are driving down a lonely stretch of road at night and see a car with its hood up and someone inside. It is too dark for you to see the person clearly, and there could be more than one. You are familiar with the road and know it is at least five miles to the nearest telephone. (Proverbs 16:7, 22:3; Matthew 10:16)

b. You are at the airport to catch a flight for an important business appointment, and you are late. You see a woman in her fifties struggling with a suitcase, and everyone is hurrying by, ignoring her pleading eyes. She is headed down a concourse to her plane, but it's the wrong concourse for your flight. As you glance at your watch, you see that your flight is scheduled to leave in five minutes, which means you should already be on the plane. You have no idea how long it will be before the next flight to your destination. (Proverbs 18:9, Matthew 5:40-42)

c. The church building needs painting, and to economize, you have been one of the "let's do it ourselves" advocates. Painting day is set for this Saturday starting at 9 a.m. and lasting until the job is done. If at least fifteen men show up for the job, it should be done by noon. It is now Thursday, and your children have just reminded you that you promised to take them and their friends to the lake on Saturday. Because of the distance involved, that means leaving before 10 a.m. (Ecclesiastes 5:5, Colossians 3:21)

God wants us to support one another.
Love will enable you to help others joyfully.

LESSON FOUR
Contributing by Support
▼

1 Briefly describe a situation where support you received
helped you through otherwise depressing circumstances.

2 Explain what Galatians 6:2 means to you.

3 Complete the following chart from 1 Thessalonians 5:14. (KJV—"feebleminded" = "fainthearted")

THE ACTION YOU ARE EXHORTED TO DO	THE TYPE OF PERSON TOWARD WHOM THIS ACTION SHOULD BE TAKEN	WHY YOU THINK THIS ACTION SHOULD BE TAKEN
Warn or admonish	*Unruly people*	*So they don't continue to be disruptive*

4 What is one important means of supporting others? (Proverbs 12:25)

5 What principles that will enable you to be supportive of others are illustrated in Isaiah 50:4-5?

6 What are some additional things you can do to support others?

Proverbs 17:22

Proverbs 19:17

Proverbs 27:5-6

Proverbs 27:9

Proverbs 31:8-9

7 a. What is the command of Romans 15:1?

b. Who do you think are the "strong"?

c. Who do you think are the "weak"?

d. Give an example of fulfilling this command.

8 a. In what circumstances do you think God wants you to do
something that would make others feel good about
themselves?

b. What are some things you could do?

9 Read 2 Kings 4:25-27.

    a. Why do you think the woman answered Gehazi as she
       did?

    b. What did you learn from this passage about people
       needing support?

10 a. What are some needs people often conceal?

    b. What are some indications of these hidden needs?

Opportunities to do good deeds are all around you.
Instead of just planning projects, you should be sensitive
to the needs of people you are with and make
good deeds a way of life.

Contributing with Comfort and Encouragement

▼

1 What were the greatest sources of comfort contributed to you by others as you faced the death of a loved one?

2 What will equip you to comfort others? (2 Corinthians 1:3-4)

3 a. What is one way you can comfort others? (1 Thessalonians 4:13-18)

b. Why do you think this will give them comfort?

4 Read 2 Corinthians 7:6-7.

a. What was the result of Paul being with Titus?

b. Why did this happen?

c. How can you be a similar encouragement or comfort to your pastor?

5 What are some things others can do or say that will encourage you?

6 How is a person needing comfort described in Psalm 77:2-6?

7 Read Matthew 26:36-45.

   a. Who needed comfort and encouragement? Why?

   b. What was done, or could have been done, to offer comfort or encouragement?

   c. What "cost" is associated with the action you just listed above?

8 a. List at least one person you know who would be encouraged, comforted, or helped by each of the following actions. (Be sure to include at least one nonChristian.)

   ☐ Sending a check for ten dollars.
   ☐ Writing a note of appreciation.
   ☐ Writing a note explaining why the person is special to you.
   ☐ Phoning long distance just to say "Hi" and "I appreciate you."

☐ Sending the book _____ (fill in the book title).
☐ Other (develop your own idea):

b. Which of the above projects do you feel God would have you complete this week?

9 What do you think is the most effective use of prayer in comforting others?

Contributing to
Spiritual Growth

▼

1 Use the concepts Paul expressed in his prayer in Colossians
1:9-12 to write a definition of spiritual growth.
(KJV—"meet" = "fit")

2 What did Paul desire for the Christians at Rome?
(Romans 1:11-12)

3 Read Philippians 1:3-11.

a. What desire did Paul have for the Philippians?

b. What did Paul do because of his desire?

c. What confidence did Paul have?

d. Why did he have this confidence?

4 a. What are you commanded to do in 1 Thessalonians 5:11?

b. What is one way God equips you for this ministry?
   (1 Peter 4:10)

5 What attitudes do you need to have if you are going to help others grow?

2 Corinthians 3:4-6

1 Corinthians 10:23-24 (KJV—"wealth" = "good")

6 What are the implications of trying to help others grow when you don't have love? (1 Corinthians 13:1-3)

7 How are gifts related to helping others grow? (Ephesians 4:11-13)

8 What actions that contribute to spiritual growth are suggested in the following verses?

2 Corinthians 4:5

Colossians 1:9

Colossians 1:28-29

2 Timothy 4:2 (KJV—"instant" = "ready")

Hebrews 10:24-25

9 Which of the above actions are you doing (can you do) in your church fellowship? Explain how they can help others grow spiritually.

10 Read Paul's address to the church leaders at Ephesus in Acts 20:28-35.

a. What command did he give?

b. What example had he set?

c. To whom and to what did he commend them? Why?

Viewing Discipline as a Contribution

▼

1 What does the term "tough love" mean to you?

2 Read Hebrews 12:5-11.

  a. Why does God discipline us?

  b. Is this reason always evident to a person undergoing discipline from God? Explain your answer.

c. List at least four other important teachings about God's discipline found in this passage.

3 What blessings for a person being chastened by God are indicated in Psalm 94:12-15?

4 a. What did God promise to David in 2 Samuel 7:14-15?

b. How do you think this applies today?

5 What is true of Christ's discipline that is not always true of rebuke by people? (Isaiah 11:3-4)

6 Use a dictionary to explain the difference between "discipline" and "punishment."

7 Does God *punish* you or does He *discipline* you for the things you do wrong? Explain your answer, using Scripture as much as possible.

8 Using the verses in Proverbs, fill in the charts that follow. (Not all of the areas will need a response.)

RESULTS OF IGNORING REPROOF	BENEFITS OF HEEDING REPROOF
Proverbs 10:17	
Proverbs 12:1	
Proverbs 13:1,18	
Proverbs 15:5,32	
Proverbs 29:1	

CHARACTERISTICS OF A PERSON WHO IGNORES REPROOF	CHARACTERISTICS OF A PERSON WHO ACCEPTS REPROOF
Proverbs 10:17	
Proverbs 12:1	
Proverbs 13:1,18	
Proverbs 15:5,32	
Proverbs 29:1	

9 What are some of the key factors that make discipline, chastisement, or rebuke a contribution and not a discouragement?

Discipline is often associated with the punishment in a medieval dungeon. But instead of being a painful experience, Christian discipline can be a positive contribution to your life; and you can use it to contribute to others.

Contributing by Discipline

▼

1 What has been the most positive experience you have had in being disciplined?

2 Whom should you rebuke? (Proverbs 9:8)

3 Do you have a responsibility to reprove others in your church? (Galatians 6:1) Explain your answer.

4 What attitudes should you have when reproving another?

2 Corinthians 2:4

Galatians 6:1

5 What two ingredients cause a reproving session to be very successful? (Proverbs 25:12)

6 a. How did Paul tell Timothy to use reproof? (1 Timothy 5:1-2)

b. How did Paul tell Titus to use reproof? (Titus 1:12-13)

c. In your opinion, why is there such a difference in these instructions?

7 Listed here are three "reproof" phrases. After each one, describe a situation when you would use the phrase.

You are wrong and need to change in . . .

You have a lot going for you, but something that may hinder your effectiveness is . . .

I could be wrong, but I get the impression that you . . .

8 In light of the clear teaching of Scripture on disciplining one another, why do you think it is practiced so little in the Body of Christ?

9 What steps for rebuke are outlined in Matthew 18:15-20?

10 How do you feel the teaching of Matthew 18:15-20 can be helpful in your church?